W9-CMM-743

Please remember
TO WASH YOUR
HANDS BEFORE
YOU READ THIS BOOK

see the ★ FiRST STAR

NORMA SIMON
PICTURES
JOE LASKER

ALBERT WHITMAN & COMPANY
CHICAGO

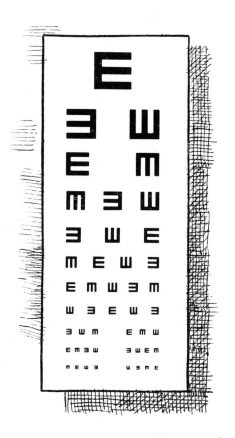

This book is dedicated to
Marie and Dr. Glass

TEXT © 1968 BY NORMA SIMON; ILLUSTRATIONS © 1968 BY JOE LASKER
LIBRARY OF CONGRESS CATALOG CARD 68-22196
PUBLISHED SIMULTANEOUSLY IN CANADA BY GEORGE J. MCLEOD, LTD., TORONTO
LITHOGRAPHED IN THE UNITED STATES OF AMERICA

A CHILD never sees through any eyes but his own. He has no way of knowing that he sees the world differently than other children do. He thinks this is the way the world looks because it is all he has ever known.

Just as adults learn to watch children for signals that suggest the unusual in growth, walking, talking, and general development, so they need to be aware of special eye signals.

A number of signals may alert an adult to difficulties. The child may, for example, rub his eyes frequently, complain that his eyes hurt, always hold his head on one side to look at things, bring his book very close to his face, have frequent headaches, or have eyes that turn in or out. Any of these signals or a combination of several mean that it is time for a careful examination by an eye doctor.

Doctors can help improve a child's eyesight and thereby change the child's outlook on the world. Doctors can help a child have the eyesight needed for school achievement. We hope this book will tell girls and boys some of the things to expect when they go for an eye examination. And we hope Johnny's story will help all children appreciate the gift of eyesight itself.

NORMA SIMON

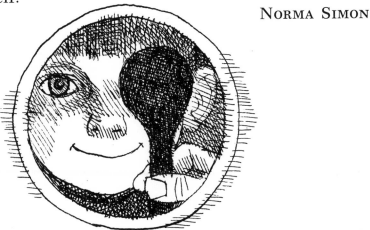

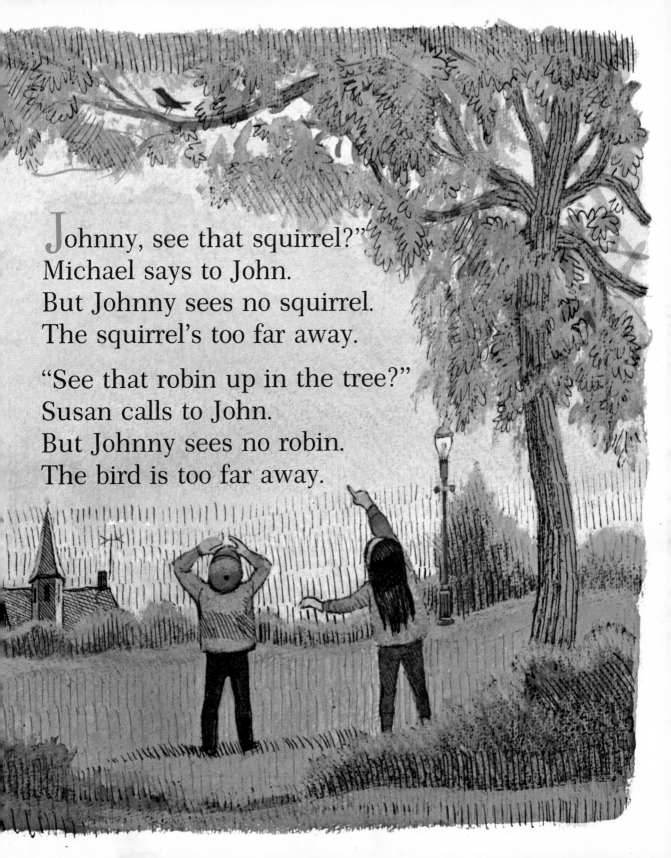

Johnny, see that squirrel?"
Michael says to John.
But Johnny sees no squirrel.
The squirrel's too far away.

"See that robin up in the tree?"
Susan calls to John.
But Johnny sees no robin.
The bird is too far away.

"See the first star shining in the sky?"
Daddy asks at night.
But Johnny sees no star.
A star is much too far.

So Daddy says to Johnny,
"See my glasses, John?"
And Johnny answers, "Yes."
"A doctor gave me my glasses
to help me see things far away."

"Can the doctor help me, Daddy?
I want to see far-away things."
That's what Johnny asks.

Daddy says, "I think so, John.
I know you'll like the doctor.
I'll take you there."

Hand in hand together,
they go to see the doctor.
A nurse in white, sitting up straight,
typing and typing very fast,
waits inside the office.

She stops her typing,
and smiles a bright smile.
She hands Johnny crayons and paper.
Then she types some more.
Johnny and Daddy wait.

The doctor opens his door.
He smiles a friendly smile.
He wears eyeglasses,
just like Johnny's dad.

"Hi, Johnny," the doctor says.
"Hi," Johnny answers back.

Then the doctor asks,
"Would you like to play
some looking games
just for you and me?"

Johnny nods his head
and takes the doctor's hand.
They go into a special room.

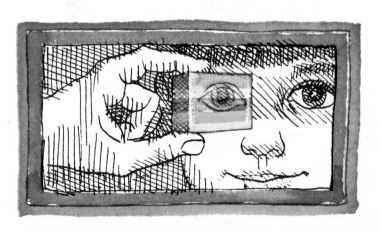

The doctor shows John
   his special instruments
   and his special machines
   and his special drops
to examine Johnny's eyes.

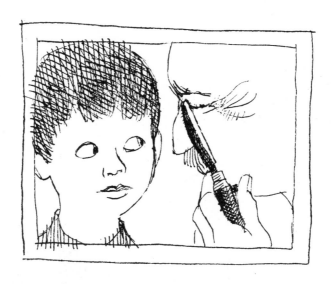

The doctor turns on one small light,
very bright.
He turns out all the other lights.
It looks like night,
except for the light across the room.

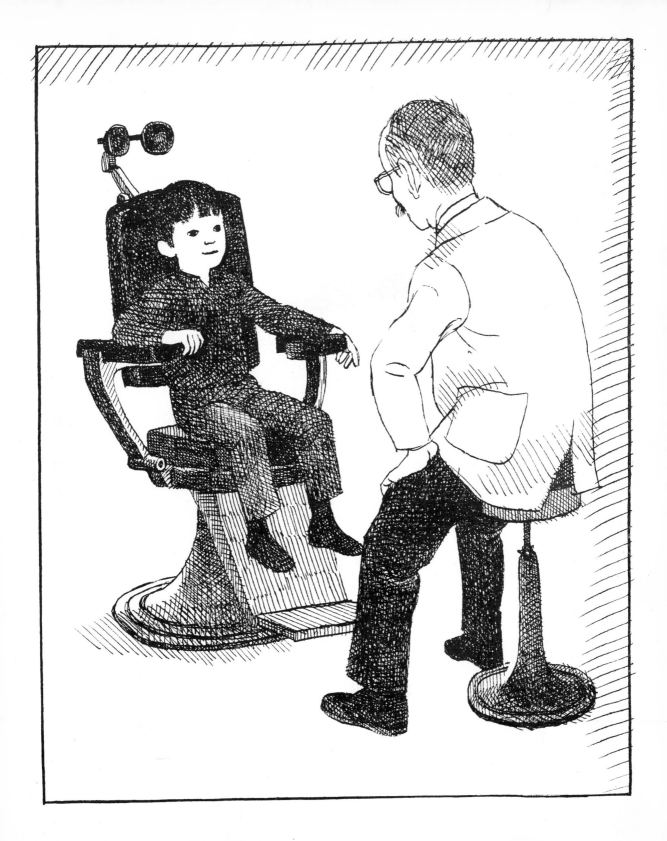

Johnny sees a picture like fingers.
The doctor says, "Please tell me how they go."
Johnny says, "Now they're pointing up.
Now they're pointing down."

Johnny likes this game. He looks and looks
and sees the fingers change.

Then he sees a ball
　　and a star
　　　and a dog
　　　　and a car
all on the wall in the bright, bright light.

And the rest of the room is just like night.

"Sometimes when you play outside,"
the doctor asks, "is it hard for you
to see things far away?"

John tells the doctor about the squirrel
too far down the road.
John tells the doctor about the robin
that flies too high in the trees.
He tells the doctor about the star
too far for him to see.

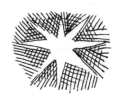

The doctor listens to everything,
and then he tells John,
"Johnny, I was just like you.
There were many things I wanted to see —
so many things too far for me.
And then I found these special windows
to look at things far away."

He takes off his eyeglasses
and shows them to John.

The doctor makes the whole room bright again.
"Everyone's eyes are different," he says.

"Different eyes need different things.
Some eyes need glasses to see far-away things.
Some eyes need glasses to see near things.
People need glasses for different reasons,
to help them see the world all around."

"If I have glasses," Johnny asks,
"just like Daddy and you,
can I see far-away things?"

"Let's try some lenses on," the doctor says,
"and see how far you see."

Johnny tries many lenses,
funny glasses with numbers all around.
Then the doctor says,
"These seem right for you."

They are funny glasses,
but Johnny wants to keep them.
He wants to take the lenses outside
to see what he can see.

"No," the doctor laughs,
"we'll leave these here with me.
You'll go to a man who will
make your glasses and <u>then</u>
you'll see how far you can see."

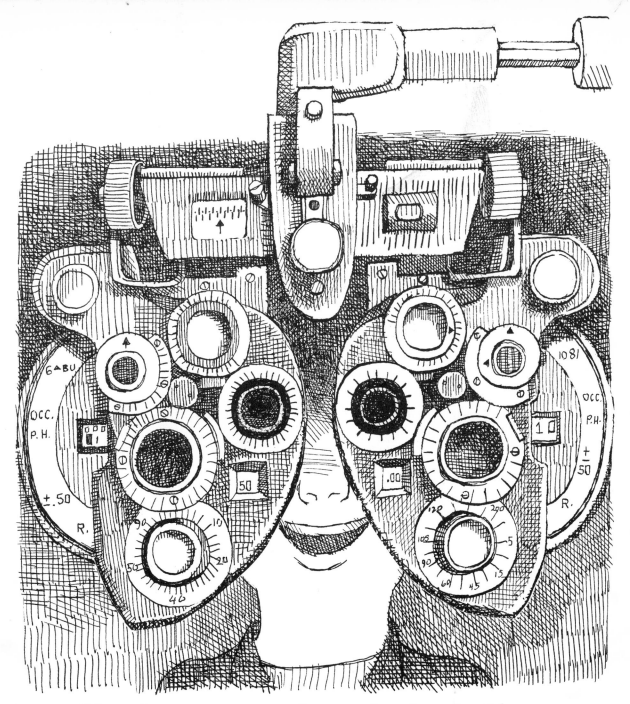

The doctor writes down the kind of lenses
Johnny needs.
He gives the paper to Johnny's dad.

Johnny and Dad say goodbye to the doctor.
The nurse waves goodbye to them, too.

The man who makes the glasses reads
the paper from the doctor.

"Now I know the lenses to make,
and you have picked out the frames.
Come back tomorrow, John," says the man.
"I'll have your new glasses ready."

The man knows it's hard for John to wait.
His dad knows it's hard for John to wait.
And John knows how hard it is to wait . . .
   for Christmas . . . for birthdays . . .
     even for tomorrow.

Morning comes, and it's time to go
to pick up Johnny's new glasses.
He tries them on —
the frames with lenses —
and they feel just fine.
He wears them out to the street.

Now
Johnny sees the red light
turn green
way far away.

He can see a dog
run across the road
way far away.
He can hear and he can see
an airplane in the sky.

When the world is dark,
Johnny looks into the night.
He sees the first star shining
in the sky.

He sees the first star
for the first time ever.
A star is far, but not too far
for Johnny to see.

Johnny feels his glasses over his eyes.
He feels his glasses over his ears,
his windows to the world far away.

It's nice to see the near things.
It's nice to see the far things.

It's nice and wonderful and grand
to see the <u>whole</u> <u>wide</u> <u>world</u>.

DEC 2

MAR 2